HOW TO DRAW FOR 10-12 YEAR OLDS

Learn to Draw Cute Animals, Dragons, Gifts and Other Cool Things

Book for Kids Age 10+

Anna Robin

What's Inside

This Book Belongs to

_____

Let's Get Drawing!

Welcome to the world of drawing! This book is made for 10–12 year olds just like you. Whether you're new to drawing or you already love to doodle, you're in the right place. Inside, you'll find step-by-step guides to help you draw all kinds of cool things — from cute animals and wild monsters to yummy snacks and awesome gadgets.

This book is all about learning while having fun. Some drawings are simple, and some are a bit more challenging. You get to pick and choose what you want to draw, so you can try new things at your own pace. As you work through the book, you'll practice key drawing skills like outlining, shading, and even making your drawings look 3D!

And remember, you don't need to be a "perfect" artist — because guess what? There's no such thing as perfect! The most important thing is to have fun and let your creativity shine. So grab your pencils, get comfy, and let's start creating some amazing art together!

What You'll Need:

- **Pencils:** A regular pencil works great, but if you have a set of drawing pencils, even better!

- **Eraser:** Don't worry if you make mistakes — it's part of the process!

- **Paper:** You can use any kind of paper you like!

- **Colored Pencils/Crayons/Markers:** If you want to add some color to your art, grab your favorite coloring tools.

And the most important tool you'll need is...

- **Your Imagination:** This is the key to everything! With your imagination, you can create anything you dream of.

How to Use This Book

This book is designed to guide you, step by step, through drawing all sorts of cool stuff. Here's how it works:

1. **Follow the steps:** Each drawing is broken down into easy steps. We'll show you what to add next with bold lines. The lighter lines show what you've already drawn.

2. **Erase as you go:** When you see dashed lines, that's your cue to erase them so your picture looks just right.

3. **Take your time:** Don't worry if it doesn't look perfect right away. Go slow and remember: practice makes progress!

4. **Make it your own:** Once you finish the steps, feel free to add your own details, colors, and style. That's what makes your art special!

Warm-Up: Draw a Bubble Number 10

Before we dive into drawing animals, monsters, and treats, let's try a quick test to warm up your drawing skills. This will help you feel confident about following the steps ahead.

Let's start with something simple — a cool 3D Bubble Number 10:

Now it's your turn

Great job! Now that you've warmed up, you're ready to tackle the fun stuff ahead!

Have Fun!

The most important thing to remember as you go through this book is to have fun. There's no need to worry about making every line or shape perfect. If something doesn't look exactly like you imagined, that's totally okay! Drawing is all about trying new things, exploring your creativity, and improving each time you practice.

Here are some helpful tips:

- **Mistakes are part of the process:** Every artist makes mistakes — even the pros! When you do, just erase and try again. It's all part of learning.

- **Experiment:** As you get more confident, try creating your own designs — mix animals, invent new monsters, or make your own dream snacks.

- **Practice:** The more you draw, the better you'll get. So don't be afraid to fill up your pages with sketches, doodles, and new ideas!

Ready to begin? Turn the page, pick a drawing, and let the adventure begin!

Cute Animals

Chipmunk

1.

2.

3.

4.

5.

6.

7.

8.

Panda

1.

2.

3.

4.

5.

6.

7.

8.

Camel

1.

2.

3.

4.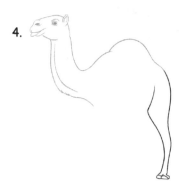

5.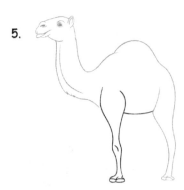

6.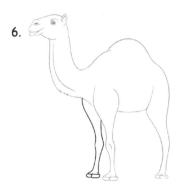

7.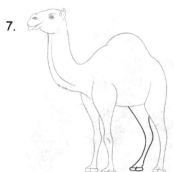

8.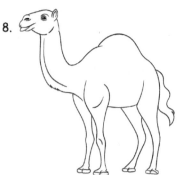

Cheetah

1.

2.

3.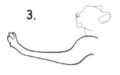

4.

5.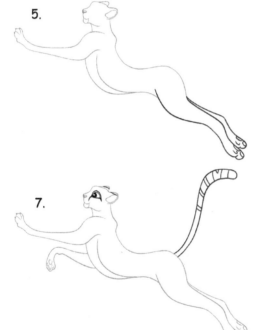

6.

7.

8.

Eagle

1.

2.

3.

4.

5.

6.

7.

8.

Giraffe

1.

2.

3.

4.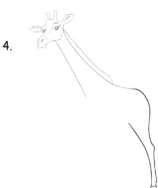

5.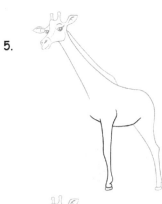

6.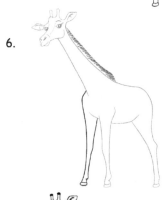

7.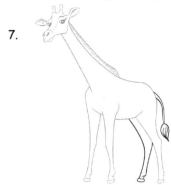

8.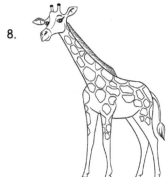

Flamingo

1.

2.

3.

4.

5.

6.

7.

8.

Peacock

1.

2.

3.

4.

5.

6.

7.

8.

Porcupine

1.

2.

3.

4.

5.

6.

7.

8.

St. Bernard Dog

1.

2.

3.

4.

5.

6.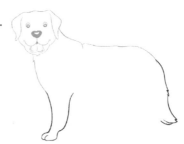

7.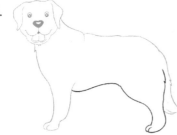

8.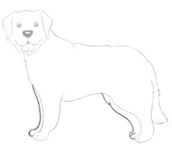

9.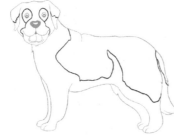

10.

Rhino

1.

2.

3.

4.

5.

6.

7.

8.

9.

10.

Husky

1.

2.

3.

4.

5.

6.

7.

8.

9.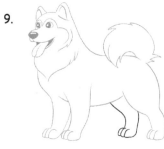

10.

Moose

1.

2.

3.

4.

5.

6.

7.

8.

9.

10.

Tiger

1.

2.

3.

4.

5.

6.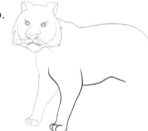

7.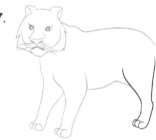

8.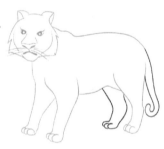

9.

10.

Now it's your turn

Now it's your turn

Under the Sea

Dolphin Pod

1.

2.

3.

4.

5.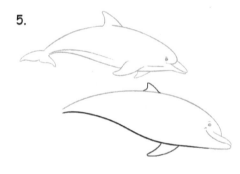

6.

7.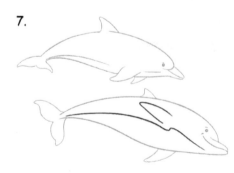

8.

Clownfish

1.

2.

3.

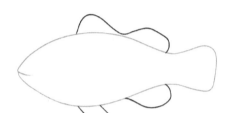

4.

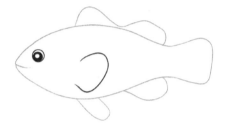

5.

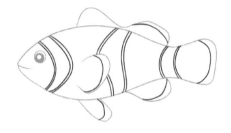

6.

7.

Great White Shark

1.

2.

3.

4.

5.

6.

7.

8.

Sea Lion

1.

2.

3.

4.

5.

6.

7.

8.

Diver

1.

2.

3.

4.

5.

6.

7.

8.

Seahorse

1.

2.

3.

4.

5.

6.

7.

8.

33

Squid

1.

2.

3.

4.

5.

6.

7.

8.

Sea Turtle

1.

2.

3.

4.

5.

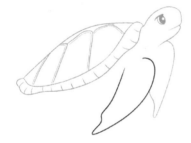

6.

7.

8.

Coral & Kelp Forest

1.

2.

3.

4.

5.

6.

7.

8.

36

Lionfish

1.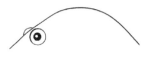

2.

3.

4.

5.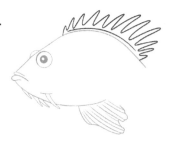

6.

7.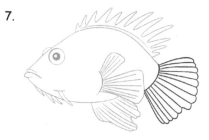

8.

9.

10.

Shipwreck

1.

2.

3.

4.

5.

6.

7.

8.

9.

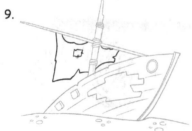

10.

Now it's your turn

Now it's your turn

Now it's your turn

Cartoon Creations

Boy's face

1.

2.

3.

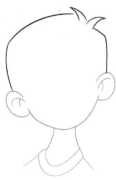

4.

5.

6.

7.

Cityscape

1.

2.

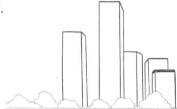

3.

4.

5.

6.

7.

45

Robot

1.

2.

3.

4.

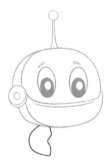

5.

6.

7.

8.

Ferris wheel

1.
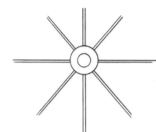

2.
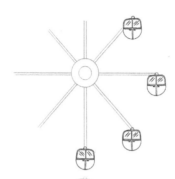

3.
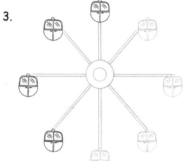

4.
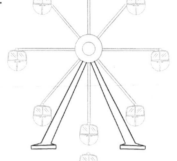

5.
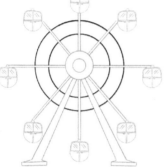

6.
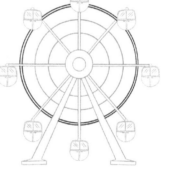

7.

Cartoon cat

1.

2.

3.

4.

5.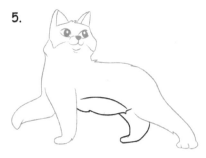

6.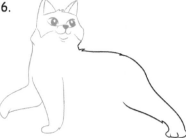

7.

8.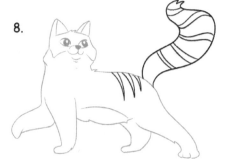

Cute monster

1.

2.

3.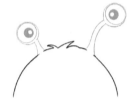

4.

5.

6.

7.

8.

Alien spaceship

1.

2.

3.

4.

5.

6.

7.

8.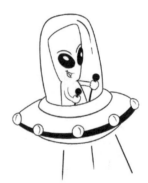

Pile of gifts

1.

2.

3.

4.

5.

6.

7.

8.

Superhero

1.

2.

3.

4.

5.

6.

7.

8.

Villain character

1.

2.

3.

4.

5.

6.

7.

8.

Friendly alien

1.

2.

3.

4.

5.

6.

7.

8.

Anime face

1.

2.

3.

4.

5.

6.

7.

8.

Magical creature

1.

2.

3.

4.

5.

6.

7.

8.

9.

10.

Now it's your turn

Now it's your turn

Now it's your turn

Thrilling Rides

Cruise Ship

1.

2.

3.

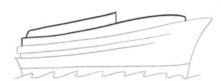

4.

5.

6.

7.

Motorbike

1.

2.

3.

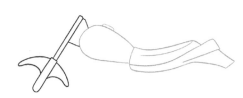

4.

5.

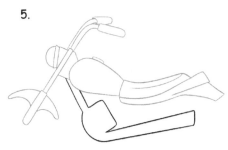

6.

7.

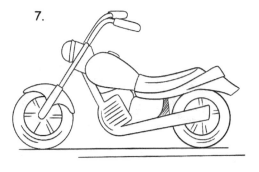

Sports car

1.

2.

3.

4.

5.

6.

7.

Helicopter

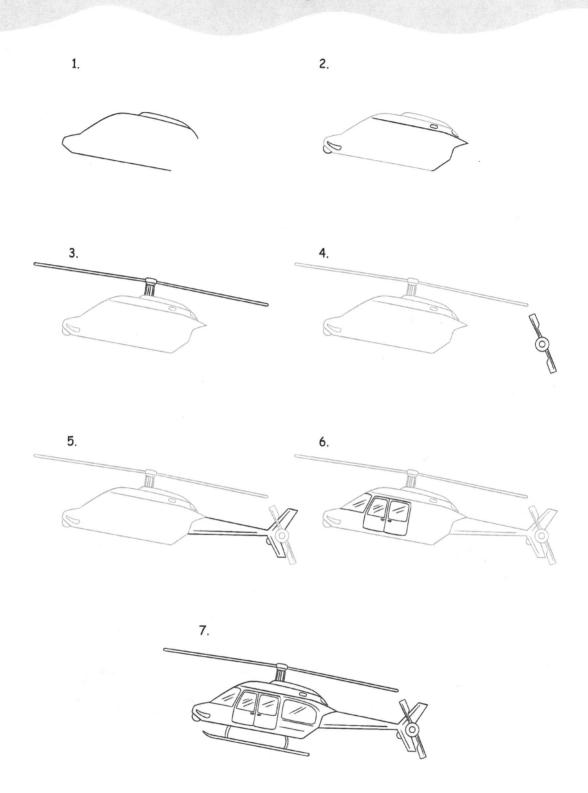

1.

2.

3.

4.

5.

6.

7.

Tractor

1.

2.

3.

4.

5.

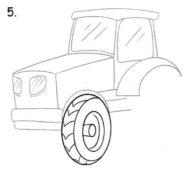

6.

7.

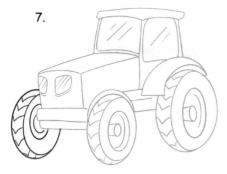

8.

Go-Kart

1.

2.

3.

4.

5.

6.

7.

8.

Monster Truck

1.

2.

3.

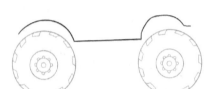

4.

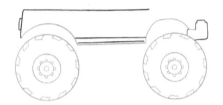

5.

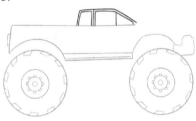

6.

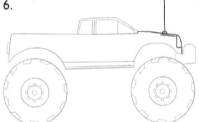

7.

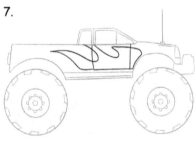

8.

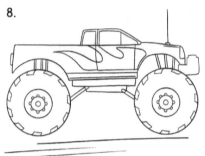

Spaceship

1.

2.

3.

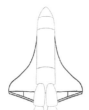

4.

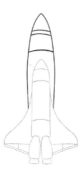

5.

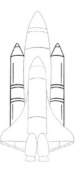

6.

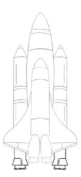

7.

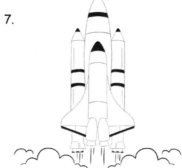

8.

Now it's your turn

Now it's your turn

Tasty Treats

Ice Cream

1.

2.

3.

4.

5.

6.

7.

Tomato

1.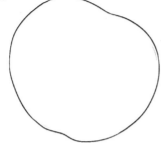

2.

3.

4.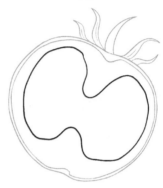

5.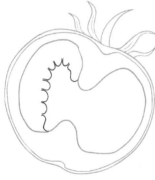

6.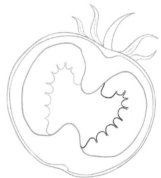

7.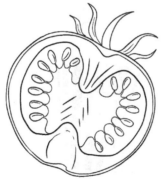

Popcorn

1.

2.

3.

4.

5.

6.

7.

Pizza Slice

1.

2.

3.

4.

5.

6.

7.

Pancakes

1.

2.

3.

4.

5.

6.

7.

Swiss Cheese

1.

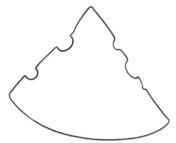

2.

3.

4.

5.

6.

7.

Bowl of Noodles

1.

2.

3.

4.

5.

6.

7.

Cheeseburger

1.

2.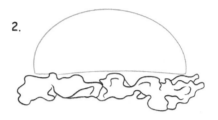

3.

4.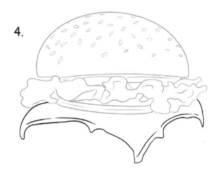

5.

6.

7.

Iced Coffee

1.
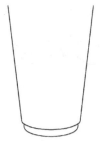

2.

3.

4.

5.

6.

7.

SuShi

1.

2.

3.

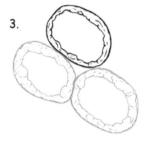

4.

5.

6.

7.

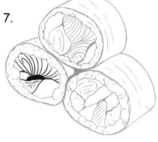

8.

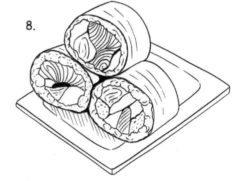

Now it's your turn

Now it's your turn

Now it's your turn.

Create your own masterpiece. Draw anything that inspires you —
a favorite scene, an original character, or a beautiful landscape.

Made in United States
Troutdale, OR
12/19/2024

26998858R00051